C000175074

REPRINT LAUNCH CARD

Title STING MERCURY FALLING PVG

Order Code   AM938014   ISBN (UK)   9780711958425

Publisher .... Binders Pack Qty

Last Printing By .... Quantity ....

Prev Unit Cost £   .98 GB Retail Price £   14.95   Size ....

Extent .... Binding .... Cover Prints ....

STOCK		COST ESTIMATE PER TITLE			
@ Launch	6 On Backorder 0	No. of Copies			
Current	6				
SALES		1.Arranging			
Current month @ Today		2.Editorial/Fees			
Last month	1				
DEC/JAN/FEB 07/08	9	3.Engraving			
06/07	2	4.Design & Paste			
Previous 1-12 months	27				
Previous 13-24 months	26	5.Photo Perms			
DISCOUNT		6.Typesetting			
Home _____ % Export _____ %		7.Origination			
ROYALTY DETAILS	Home Export	Preproduction Sub total			
Rate	14.99 % 14.99 %				
Value £	2.24 2.24	Paper			
Proposed Print		Board			
Proposed Price		8.Paper Sub total			
Income per Copy		Text Print			
Royalty per copy		Illus Print			
Net income		Cover Print			
Gross Profit		Binding			
Gross Profit %		Other			
ACTION		9.Manu Sub Total			
Copies _____ Price _____		TOTAL COST			
F.D _____ __/__/__		UNIT COST			
M.D _____ __/__/__					
S.D _____ __/__/__					

STING

mercury falling

MAGNETIC PUBLISHING LIMITED

Exclusive Distributors:
Music Sales Limited
8/9 Frith Street, London W1V 5TZ, England.
Music Sales Pty Limited
120 Rothschild Avenue, Rosebery, NSW 2018, Australia.

Order No.AM938014
ISBN 0-7119-5842-4

Visit the Music Sales' Internet Music Shop at
http://www.musicsales.co.uk

Book design by Michael Bell Design.
Music arranged by Roger Day.
Music processed by Paul Ewers Music Design.

Printed in the United Kingdom by
Caligraving Limited, Brunel Way,
Thetford, Norfolk.

Music Sales' complete catalogue describes
thousands of titles and is available in full colour
sections by subject, direct from Music Sales Limited.
Please state your areas of interest and send
a cheque/postal order for £1.50 for postage to:
Music Sales Limited, Newmarket Road,
Bury St. Edmunds, Suffolk IP33 3YB.

mercury falling

The hounds of winter

Mercury falling
I rise from my bed
Collect my thoughts together
I have to hold my head
It seems that she's gone
And somehow I am pinned by
The hounds of winter
Howling in the wind.

I walk through the day
My coat around my ears
I look for my companion
I have to dry my tears
It seems that she's gone
Leaving me too soon
I'm as dark as December
I'm as cold as the man in the moon
I still see her face
As beautiful as day
It's easy to remember
Remember my love that way.
All I hear is that lonesome sound
And the hounds of winter they follow me down.

I can't make up the fire
The way that she could
I spend all my days
In the search for dry wood
Board all the windows
And close the front door
I can't believe
She won't be here anymore.

A season for joy
A season for sorrow
Where she's gone
I will surely, surely follow
She brightened my day
She warmed the coldest night
The hounds of winter
They got me in their sights.

I hung my head

Early one morning
With time to kill
I borrowed Jeb's rifle
And sat on the hill
I saw a lone rider
Crossing the plain
I drew a bead on him
To practise my aim
My brother's rifle
Went off in my hand
A shot rang out
Across the land,
The horse kept on running
The rider was dead
I hung my head, I hung my head.

I set off running
To wake from my dream
My brother's rifle

Went into the stream
I kept on running
Into the salt lands
And that's where they found me
My head in my hands.
The sheriff he asked me
Why had I run
Then it came to me
Just what I had done
And all for no reason
Just one piece of lead
I hung my head, I hung my head.

Here in the courthouse
The whole town is here
I see the judge
High up in his chair
"Explain to the courtroom
What went through your mind
And we'll ask the jury
What verdict they find."
I said "I felt the power
Of death over life
I orphaned his children
I widowed his wife.
I beg their forgiveness
I wish I was dead."
I hung my head, I hung my head.

Early one morning
With time to kill
I see the gallows
Up on the hill
And out in the distance
A trick of the brain
I see a lone rider
Crossing the plain.
He's come to fetch me
To see what they done
We'll ride together
Till kingdom come
I pray for God's mercy
For soon I'll be dead
I hung my head, I hung my head.

Let your soul be your pilot

Let your soul be your pilot
Let your soul guide you upon your way.

When you're down and they're counting
When you're secret's all found out
When your troubles take to mounting
When the map you have leads you to doubt
When there's no information and the compass turns
To nowhere that you know well
Let your soul be your pilot
Let your soul guide you
He'll guide you well.

When the doctors failed to heal you
When no medicine chest can make you well
When no counsel leads to comfort
When there are no more lies they can tell
No more useless information

And the compass spins
The compass spins between heaven and hell
Let your soul be your pilot
Let your soul guide you
He'll guide you well.

And your eyes turn toward the window pane
To the lights upon the hill
The distance seems so strange to you now
And the dark room seems so still.

Let your pain be my sorrow
Let your tears be my tears too
Let your courage be my model
That the north you find will be true
When there's no more information
And the compass turns to nowhere that you know well
Let your soul be your pilot
Let your soul guide you
Let your soul guide you
Let your soul guide you upon your way
Let your soul guide you along the way
Let your soul guide you along the way
Let your soul guide you along the way
Let your soul guide you along the way.

i was brought to my senses

Alone with my thoughts this evening
I walked on the banks of Tyne
I wondered how I could win you
Or if I could make you mine
Or if I could make you mine.

The wind it was so insistent
With tales of a stormy south
But when I spied two birds in a sycamore tree
There came a dryness in my mouth
Came a dryness in my mouth.

For then without rhyme or reason
The two birds did rise up and fly
And when the two birds were flying
I swear I saw you and I
I swear I saw you and I.

I walked out this morning
It was like a veil had been removed from before my eyes
For the first time I saw the work of heaven
In the line where the hills had been married to the sky
And all around me ev'ry blade of singing grass
Was calling out your name
And that our love would always last
And inside ev'ry turning leaf
Is the pattern of an older tree
The shape of our future
The shape of all our history
And out of the confusion
Where the river meets the sea
Came things I'd never seen
Things I'd never seen.

I was brought to my senses
I was blind but now I can see
Ev'ry signpost in nature
Said you belong to me.

I know it's true
It's written in a sky as blue
As blue as your eyes, as blue as your eyes
If nature's red in tooth and claw
Like winter's freeze and summer's thaw
The wounds she gave me
Were the wounds that would heal me
And we'd be like the moon and sun
And when our courtly dance had run
Its course across the sky
Then together we would lie
And out of the confusion
Where the river meets the sea
Something new would arrive
Something better would arrive.

I was brought to my senses
I was blind but now I can see
Ev'ry signpost in nature
Said you belong to me.

I was brought to my senses
I was blind but now I can see
Ev'ry signpost in nature
Said you belong to me.

you still touch me

Another night finds me alone
In my dreams you still touch me
Your picture by my telephone
In that smile you still thrill me

Now if I sleep, I sleep here alone
In my bed tonight, you still haunt me
And if I'm falling, I'm falling like a stone
And in my nightmare you still hold me.

And after all that we've been through
Now I'm wond'ring if you still blame me
If only half of this was true
That you believe of me you still shame me.

Dark rain will fall until I see your face
I close my eyes, I seem to hear the raindrops saying
you won't come back
You still touch me.

And when I'm sick at heart and low
In my prayers you still heal me
When I'm so sure this isn't so
In my complacency you still shake me.

I wonder if you feel the same way as I do
And you'd come back
You still touch me.

Another night finds me alone
In my bed tonight, you still haunt me
You still hold me
You still touch me
You still touch me
You still touch me.

Another night, another night
Another night, another night finds me alone.

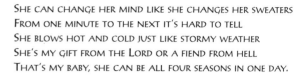

i'm so happy i can't stop crying

SEVEN WEEKS HAVE PAST NOW SINCE SHE LEFT ME
AND SHE SHOWS HER FACE TO ASK ME HOW I AM
SHE SAYS THE KIDS ARE FINE AND THAT THEY MISS ME
MAYBE I COULD COME AND BABYSIT SOME TIME.

SHE SAYS "ARE YOU OK? I WAS WORRIED ABOUT YOU
CAN YOU FORGIVE ME? I HOPE THAT YOU'LL BE HAPPY"
I SAID "I'M SO HAPPY THAT I CAN'T STOP CRYING
I'M SO HAPPY, I'M LAUGHING THROUGH MY TEARS."

I SAW A FRIEND OF MINE. HE SAID "I WAS WORRIED ABOUT YOU
I HEARD SHE HAD ANOTHER MAN. I WONDERED HOW YOU FELT ABOUT IT"
I'M SO HAPPY THAT I CAN'T STOP CRYING
I'M SO HAPPY I'M LAUGHING THROUGH MY TEARS.

SAW MY LAWYER, MR. GOOD NEWS
HE GOT ME JOINT CUSTODY AND LEGAL SEPARATION
I'M SO HAPPY THAT I CAN'T STOP CRYING
I'M SO HAPPY I'M LAUGHING THROUGH MY TEARS, I'M LAUGHING
  THROUGH MY TEARS.

I TOOK A WALK ALONE LAST NIGHT, I LOOKED UP AT THE STARS
TO TRY AND FIND AN ANSWER IN MY LIFE
I CHOSE A STAR FOR ME, I CHOSE A STAR FOR HIM
I CHOSE TWO STARS FOR MY KIDS AND ONE STAR FOR MY WIFE
SOMETHING MADE ME SMILE
SOMETHING SEEMED TO EASE THE PAIN
SOMETHING 'BOUT THE UNIVERSE
AND HOW IT'S ALL CONNECTED.

THE PARK IS FULL OF SUNDAY FATHERS AND MELTED ICE CREAM
WE TRY TO DO THE BEST WITHIN THE GIVEN TIME
A KID SHOULD BE WITH HIS MOTHER, EVERYBODY KNOWS THAT
WHAT CAN A FATHER DO BUT BABYSIT SOME TIMES
I SAW THAT FRIEND OF MINE HE SAID "YOU LOOK DIFF'RENT SOME HOW"
I SAID "EV'RYBODY'S GOT TO LEAVE THE DARKNESS SOMETIMES".

I SAID "I'M SO HAPPY THAT I CAN'T STOP CRYING
I'M LAUGHING THROUGH MY TEARS, I'M LAUGHING THROUGH MY TEARS."

all four seasons

WITH HER SMILE AS SWEET AS A WARM WIND IN SUMMER
SHE'S GOT ME FLYING LIKE A BIRD IN A BRIGHT JUNE SKY
AND THEN JUST WHEN SHE THINKS THAT I'VE GOT HER NUMBER
BRINGS ME DOWN TO THE GROUND WITH A WINTRY EYE
THAT'S MY BABY, SHE CAN BE ALL FOUR SEASONS IN ONE DAY.

AND WHEN THE NIGHT TIME COMES WITH NO INTERFERENCE
TO OUR WARM SUMMER LOVE WITH ALL ITS CHARMS
BUT LIKE A THOROUGHBRED HORSE SHE CAN TURN ON A SIXPENCE
AND I FIND THAT I'M BACK IN MISTRESS WINTER'S ARMS
THAT'S MY BABY, SHE CAN BE ALL FOUR SEASONS IN ONE DAY.

HOW WILL I KNOW, HOW CAN I TELL
WHICH SIDE OF THE BED SHE TAKES WHEN THE DAY BEGINS?
SHE CAN BE KIND, SHE CAN BE CRUEL
SHE GOT ME GUESSING LIKE A GAME SHOW FOOL.

SHE CAN CHANGE HER MIND LIKE SHE CHANGES HER SWEATERS
FROM ONE MINUTE TO THE NEXT IT'S HARD TO TELL
SHE BLOWS HOT AND COLD JUST LIKE STORMY WEATHER
SHE'S MY GIFT FROM THE LORD OR A FIEND FROM HELL
THAT'S MY BABY, SHE CAN BE ALL FOUR SEASONS IN ONE DAY.

WATCHING THE WEATHER MAN'S BEEN NO GOOD AT ALL
WINTER, SPRING, SUMMER, I'M BOUND FOR A FALL
NO LONG TERM PREDICTION FOR MY BABY
SHE CAN BE ALL FOUR SEASONS IN ONE DAY.

HOW WILL I KNOW, HOW CAN I TELL
WHICH SIDE OF THE BED SHE TAKES WHEN THE DAY BEGINS?
SHE CAN BE KIND, SHE CAN BE CRUEL
SHE GOT ME GUESSING LIKE A GAME SHOW FOOL.

IF IT'S A SUNNY DAY I TAKE MY UMBRELLA
JUST IN CASE THE RAINDROPS START TO FALL
YOU COULD SAY THAT I'M JUST A CAUTIOUS FELLOW
I DON'T WANT TO BE CAUGHT IN A SUDDEN SQUALL
THAT'S MY BABY, SHE CAN BE ALL FOUR SEASONS IN ONE DAY.
THAT'S MY BABY, SHE CAN BE ALL FOUR SEASONS IN ONE DAY.

twenty five to midnight

THE TRAIN I RIDE DON'T BE SLOW
IF YOUR WHISTLE CAN BLOW
FIFTEEN MILES DOWN THE TRACK
TELL THEM I'M COMING BACK
COUNTING POLES, COUNTING SHEEP
DON'T BE SLOW, I WON'T WEEP
IF YOUR WHEELS ON THE LINE
WERE TO PUT ME ON TIME.

JUST A YEAR TO THE DAY
SINCE I WENT UPON MY WAY
SEEK MY FORTUNE AND FAME
BE A STAR, CHANGE MY NAME
AND THAT'S IT MORE OR LESS
TILL THIS MIDNIGHT EXPRESS
I KNOW I CAN'T BE LATE
'CAUSE SHE SAID SHE WON'T WAIT
SHE'LL JUST GO MARRY JACK
SO THERE'S NO TURNING BACK
AND IT'S TWENTY FIVE TO MIDNIGHT
AND FIFTEEN MILES OF TRACK.

BAND I HAD GOT A BREAK
JUST ONE CHANCE WE HAD TO TAKE
TOLD MY GIRL I'D BE BACK
LEFT HER WITH MY FRIEND JACK
NEW YORK CITY FOR A SPELL
THINGS DIDN'T TURN OUT SO WELL
EVERY DIVE THAT WE PLAYED
WE WERE LUCKY TO GET PAID.

MR. TRAIN DRIVER PLEASE
IF YOUR SPEED YOU INCREASE
EVERY CENT I HAVE NOW
WILL BE YOURS, THIS I VOW
AND THAT'S IT, MORE OR LESS

TILL THIS MIDNIGHT EXPRESS
I KNOW I CAN'T BE LATE
'CAUSE SHE SAID SHE WON'T WAIT
SHE'LL JUST GO MARRY JACK
SO THERE'S NO TURNING BACK
AND IT'S TWENTY FIVE TO MIDNIGHT
AND FIFTEEN MILES OF TRACK.

WE CALLED OURSELVES THE LATINO LOVERS
HAWAIIAN SHORTS AND TOP FORTY COVERS
I DIDN'T THINK I COULD SINK THIS LOW
WHEN DRUGS AND BOOZE ATE ALL MY DOUGH
THIS ISN'T HOW IT WAS MEANT TO BE
THERE'S NO SUCH THING AS A MEAL THAT'S FREE
IF I WAS EVER TO GET OUT ALIVE
I HAVE TO GET HOME ON TIME.

TRAIN I RIDE DON'T BE SLOW
IF YOUR WHISTLE CAN BLOW
FIFTY MILES DOWN THE TRACK
TELL THEM I'M COMING BACK
AND THAT'S IT, MORE OR LESS
TILL THIS MIDNIGHT EXPRESS
I KNOW I CAN'T BE LATE
'CAUSE SHE SAID SHE WON'T WAIT
SHE'LL JUST GO MARRY JACK
SO THERE'S NO TURNING BACK
AND IT'S TWENTY FIVE TO MIDNIGHT
AND FIFTEEN MILES OF TRACK
TWENTY FIVE TO MIDNIGHT
AND FIFTEEN MILES OF TRACK.

La Belle Dame sans regrets

DANSONS TU DIS
ET MOI, JE SUIS MES PASSONT GAUCHES
MES PIEDS TU FAUCHES
JE CRAINS LES SOTS
JE CHERCHE EN VAIN LES MOTS
POUR M'EXPLIQUER TA VIE
ALORS, TUMENTS MA SŒUR.

TU BRISES MON CŒUR
JE PENSE, TU SAIS
ERREURS, JAMAIS
J'ÉCOUTE TU PARLES
JE NE COMPRENDS PAS BIEN
LA BELLE DAME SANS REGRETS
LA BELLE DAME SANS REGRETS.

JE PLEURE, TU RIS
JE CHANTE, TU CRIES
TU SÈMES LES GRAINES
D'UN MAUVAIS CHÊNE
TU EN A RAS LE BOL
J'ATTENDS TOUJOURS
MES CRIS SONT SOURDS.

TU MENTS, MA SŒUR
TU BRISES MON CŒUR
JE PENSE, TU SAIS
ERREURS, JAMAIS
J'ÉCOUTE TU PARLES

JE NE COMPRENDS PAS BIEN
LA BELLE DAME SANS REGRETS
LA BELLE DAME SANS REGRETS
LA BELLE DAME SANS REGRETS.

Valparaiso

CHASE THE DOG STAR
OVER THE SEA
HOME WHERE MY TRUE LOVE IS WAITING FOR ME
ROPE THE SOUTH WIND
CANVAS THE STARS
HARNESS THE MOONLIGHT
SO SHE CAN SAFELY GO
ROUND THE CAPE HORN TO VALPARAISO.

RED THE PORT LIGHT
STARBOARD THE GREEN
HOW WILL SHE KNOW OF THE DEVILS I'VE SEEN?
CROSS THE SKY
STAR OF THE SEA
UNDER THE MOONLIGHT
THERE SHE CAN SAFELY GO
ROUND THE CAPE HORN TO VALPARAISO.

VALPARAISO
AND EVERY ROAD I WALKED WOULD TAKE ME DOWN TO THE SEA
WITH EVERY BROKEN PROMISE IN MY SACK
AND EVERY LOVE WOULD ALWAYS SEND THE SHIP OF MY HEART
OVER THE ROLLING SEA

IF I SHOULD DIE
AND WATER'S MY GRAVE
SHE'LL NEVER KNOW IF I'M DAMNED OR I'M SAVED
SEE THE GHOST
OVER THE SEA
UNDER THE MOONLIGHT
THERE SHE CAN SAFELY GO
ROUND THE CAPE HORN TO VALPARAISO.

VALPARAISO VALPARAISO
VALPARAISO.

Lithium sunset

FILL MY EYES O LITHIUM SUNSET
AND TAKE THIS LONESOME BURDEN OF WORRY FROM MY MIND
TAKE THIS HEARTACHE OF OBSIDIAN DARKNESS
AND FOLD MY DARKNESS INSIDE YOUR YELLOW LIGHT.

I'VE BEEN SCATTERED, I'VE BEEN SHATTERED,
I'VE BEEN KNOCKED OUT OF THE RACE
BUT I'LL GET BETTER
I FEEL YOUR LIGHT UPON MY FACE.

HEAL MY SOUL O LITHIUM SUNSET
AND I'LL RIDE THE TURNING WORLD INTO ANOTHER NIGHT
INTO ANOTHER NIGHT, INTO ANOTHER NIGHT.

SEE MERCURY FALLING, SEE MERCURY FALLING
SEE MERCURY FALLING, SEE MERCURY FALLING.

the hounds of winter

Words & Music by Sting

Mer - cu - ry fall - ing, I rise from— my bed,—

col - lect my thoughts to - ge - ther, I have to hold my head,—

it seems that she's gone and some-how I___ am pinned_ by

the hounds of win-ter, howl-ing in the wind.

I walk_ through the day, my coat a-round_ my ears,_____
(Verses 2 & 3 see block lyric)

I look for my com-pan-ion I have to dry my tears,_

Verse 2:
I can't make up the fire
The way that she could
I spend all my days
In the search for dry wood
Board all the windows
And close the front door
I can't believe
She won't be here anymore.

Verse 3:
A season for joy
A season for sorrow
Where she's gone
I will surely, surely follow
She brightened my day
She warmed the coldest night
The hounds of winter
They got me in their sights.

I Hung My Head

WORDS & MUSIC BY STING

Early one morning with time to kill_____ I
(Verses 2, 3 & 4 see block lyric)

borrowed Jeb's rifle and sat on the hill,_____ I

13

Repeat to fade

hung my head,_____ I hung my head._____ I

Verse 2:
I set off running
To wake from my dream
My brother's rifle
Went into the stream
I kept on running
Into the salt lands
And that's where they found me
My head in my hands.
The sheriff he asked me
Why had I run
Then it came to me
Just what I had done
And all for no reason
Just one piece of lead
I hung my head, I hung my head

Verse 3:
Here in the courthouse
The whole town is here
I see the judge
High up in his chair
"Explain to the courtroom
What went through your mind
And we'll ask the jury
What verdict they find."
I said "I felt the power
Of death over life
I orphaned his children
I widowed his wife.
I beg their forgiveness
I wish I was dead."
I hung my head, I hung my head.

Verse 4:
Early one morning
With time to kill
I see the gallows
Up on the hill
And out in the distance
A trick of the brain
I see a lone rider
Crossing the plain.
He's come to fetch me
To see what they done
We'll ride together
Till kingdom come
I pray for God's mercy
For soon I'll be dead
I hung my head, I hung my head.

Let your soul be your pilot

Words & Music by Sting

dow pane   to the lights__ up - on the hill.

The dis - tance seems so strange to you now and the dark room__ seems so

D.%. al Coda   ⊕ **Coda**

still.   3. Let your   Let your

soul guide__ you,   let your soul guide__ you

up-on— your way. Let your soul guide you a - long the way,

let your soul guide you a - long the way. Let your soul guide you a -

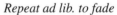

Repeat ad lib. to fade

long the way, let your soul guide you a - long the way.

Verse 2:

When the doctors failed to heal you
When no medicine chest can make you well.
When no counsel leads to comfort
When there are no more lies they can tell.
No more useless information
And the compass spins,
The compass spins between heaven and hell
Let your soul be your pilot
Let your soul guide you
He'll guide you well.

Verse 3:

Let your pain be my sorrow
Let your tears be my tears too.
Let your courage be my model
That the north you find will be true.
When there's no more information
And the compass turns to nowhere that you know well
Let your soul be your pilot
Let your soul guide you…
To Coda

i was brought to my senses

WORDS & MUSIC BY STING

1. I walked out this morn-ing— it was like a veil had been re-moved from be-fore my eyes.

long to me.)

(Verse 2 see block lyric)

I can see— ev-'ry sign - - - - post in na - ture— said
you— be you— be - - long— to— I was

At **A**

Verse 2:

The wind it was so insistent
With tales of a stormy south
But when I spied two birds in a sycamore tree
There came a dryness in my mouth,
Came a dryness in my mouth.

Verse 3:

For then without rhyme or reason
The two birds did rise up and fly
And where the two birds were flying
I swear I saw you and I,
I swear I saw you and I.

At **B**

Verse 2:

I know it's true
It's written in a sky as blue
As blue as your eyes, as blue as your eyes
If nature's red in tooth and claw
Like winter's freeze and summer's thaw
The wounds she gave me
Were the wounds that would heal me
And we'd be like the moon and sun
And when our courtly dance had run
Its course across the sky
Then together we would lie
And out of the confusion
Where the river meets the sea
Something new would arrive,
Something better would arrive.

you still touch me

WORDS & MUSIC BY STING

An-oth-er night finds me a-lone_____ in my dreams,_____ you still touch me,_____

and if I'm fall - ing, I'm fall - ing like a stone.

In my night - mare,___ you still hold me.___

1. And af - ter all that we've been
(Verse 2 see block lyric)

through,___ now I'm won - - d'ring___

Verse 2:
And when I'm sick at heart and low
In my prayers
You still heal me
When I'm so sure this isn't so
In my complacency
You still shake me.

i'm so happy i can't stop crying

WORDS & MUSIC BY STING

I'm so hap - py, I'm laugh - ing through my _____ tears."

3.

can't _ stop cry - - - ing, I'm laugh - ing through _

_____ my tears, I'm laugh - ing through _ my tears.

I took a walk a - lone _ last night, _ I

looked up at___ the stars,___ to try and find___ an ans-
- wer in___ my___ life. I chose a
star for me,___ I chose a star for him,___
I chose two___ stars for my kids and one___ star for my wife..

Some-thing made me smile, some-thing seemed to ease the pain, some-thing 'bout the u-ni-verse and how it's all con-nec-ted.

Verse 2:
I saw a friend of mine. He said "I was worried about you,
I heard she had another man. I wondered how you felt about it"
I'm so happy that I can't stop crying,
I'm so happy I'm laughing through my tears.

Verse 3:
Saw my lawyer, Mr. Good News
He got me joint custody and legal separation.
I'm so happy that I can't stop crying,
I'm laughing through my tears, I'm laughing through my tears.

twenty five to midnight

WORDS & MUSIC BY STING

1. The train I ride don't be slow, if your
(Verse 2 see block lyric)

whis - tle can blow, fif - teen miles down the track. Tell them

I'm com - ing back. Count - ing poles count - ing sheep don't be

slow I won't weep, if your wheels on the line were to

put me on time. Just a year to the day since I

(Verse 3 see block lyric)

went up-on my way seek my for - tune and fame, be a

star, change my name, and that's it more or less till this

We called our-selves the la-ti - no lo-vers, Ha-wai-ian shorts and top for - ty co-vers,

I did-n't think I could sink— this low— when drugs and booze ate all— my dough.-

This is-n't how it was meant— to be,— there's no such thing as a meal that's free.—

If I was ev-er to get out a-live— I have to get home on time.- 3. Train I

⊕ *Coda*

twen-ty five— to— mid - night———— and fif-teen miles— of track,—

twen-ty five— to— mid - night———— and fif-teen miles— of track.—

Verse 2:

Band I had got a break
Just one chance we had to take
Told my girl I'd be back
Left her with my friend Jack
New York City for a spell
Things didn't turn out so well
Every dive that we played
We were lucky to get paid.

Mr. Train Driver, please
If your speed you increase
Every cent I have now
Will be yours, this I vow
And that's it, more or less
Till this midnight express
I know I can't be late
'Cause she said she won't wait
She'll just go marry Jack
So there's no turning back
And it's 25 to midnight and 15 miles of track.

Verse 3: (D.%.)

Train I ride don't be slow
If your whistle can blow
50 miles down the track
Tell them I'm coming back
And that's it, more or less
Till this midnight express
I know I can't be late
'Cause she said she won't wait
She'll just go marry Jack
So there's no turning back
And it's 25 to midnight and 15 miles of track.
To Coda

all four seasons

Words & Music by Sting

1. With her smile as sweet as a warm wind in sum-mer, she's got me
(Verses 2, 3 & 4 see block lyric)

fly-ing like a bird in a bright June sky,— and— then just when she thinks that

all   four   sea - sons   in   one   day.)

Verse 2:
And when the night time comes with no interference
To our warm summer love with all its charms
But like a thoroughbred horse she can turn on a sixpence
And I find that I'm back in Mistress Winter's arms
That's my baby
She can be all four seasons in one day.

Verse 3:
She can change her mind like she changes her sweaters
From one minute to the next it's hard to tell
She blows hot and cold just like stormy weather
She's my gift from the Lord or a fiend from hell
That's my baby
She can be all four seasons in one day.

Verse 4:
If it's a sunny day I take my umbrella
Just in case the raindrops start to fall
You could say that I'm just a cautious fellow
I don't want to be caught in a sudden squall
That's my baby
She can be all four seasons in one day.

La Belle Dame Sans Regrets

WORDS & MUSIC BY STING & DOMINIC MILLER

Dan - sons

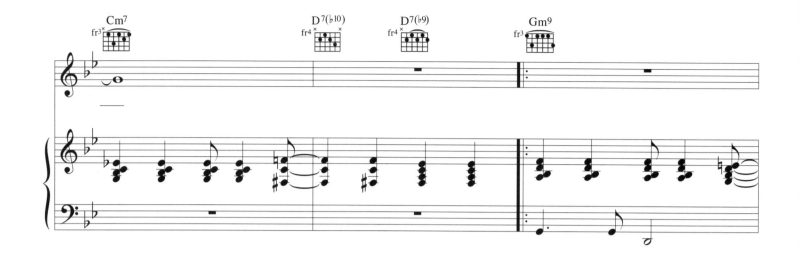

Repeat ad lib. to fade

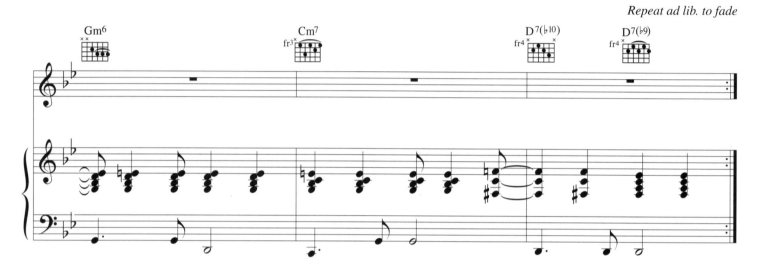

Verse 3:
Je pleure, tu ris
Je chante, tu cries
Tu sèmes les graines
D'un mauvais chêne
Tu en a ras le bol
J'attends toujours,
Mes cris sont sourds.

Verse 4:
Tu ments, ma Sœur
Tu brises mon cœur
Je pense, tu sais
Erreurs, jamais
J'écoute, tu parles
Je ne comprends pas bien
La belle dame sans regrets.

valparaiso

WORDS & MUSIC BY STING

Chase the dog star over the sea,
(Verses 2 & 3 see block lyric)

home where my true love is wait-ing for

Verse 2:
Red the port light
Starboard the green
How will she know of the devils I've seen?
Cross the sky
Star of the sea
Under the moonlight
There she can safely go
Round the Cape Horn to Valparaiso.

Verse 3:
If I should die
And water's my grave
She'll never know if I'm damned or I'm saved.
See the ghost
Over the sea
Under the moonlight
There she can safely go
Round the Cape Horn to Valparaiso.

Lithium sunset

Words & Music by Sting

1/97 (26742)